ISSUES
&Physical Science

FORCE AND MOTION

SCIENCE
EDUCATION FOR
PUBLIC
UNDERSTANDING
PROGRAM

SEPUP

UNIVERSITY OF CALIFORNIA AT BERKELEY
LAWRENCE HALL OF SCIENCE

LAB-AIDS
INCORPORATED
RONKONKOMA, NEW YORK

This book is part of SEPUP's middle school
science course sequence:

Issues and Earth Science

Rocks, Minerals, and Soils
Shaping the Land
Weather and Atmosphere
The Earth in Space
Exploring the Solar System

Issues and Life Science

My Body and Me
Micro-Life
Our Genes, Our Selves
Ecology and Evolution
Using Tools and Ideas

Issues and Physical Science

Properties of Materials
Water
Energy
Force and Motion

Additional SEPUP instructional materials include:
CHEM-2 (Chemicals, Health, Environment and Me): Grades 4–6
SEPUP Modules: Grades 7–12
Science and Sustainability: Course for Grades 9–12

This material is based upon work supported by the National Science
Foundation under Grants No. 9252906 and No. 0099265. Any opinions,
findings, and conclusions or recommendations expressed in this material
are those of the authors and do not necessarily reflect the views of the
National Science Foundation.

The preferred citation format for this book is
SEPUP. (2006). *Issues and Physical Science*. Lawrence Hall of Science, University of
California at Berkeley. Published by Lab-Aids®, Inc., Ronkonkoma, NY

SEPUP
Lawrence Hall of Science
University of California at Berkeley
Berkeley CA 94720-5200

e-mail: sepup@berkeley.edu
Website: www.sepuplhs.org

Published by:

17 Colt Court
Ronkonkoma NY 11779
Website: www.lab-aids.com

A Letter to *Issues and Physical Science* Students

As you examine the activities in this book, you may wonder, "Why does this book look so different from other science books I've seen?" The reason is simple: it is a different kind of science program, and only some of what you will learn can be seen by leafing through this book!

Issues and Physical Science uses several kinds of activities to teach science. For example, you will observe and test the properties of elements and compounds. You will model the atoms and molecules that make up these substances. You will design and conduct investigations to explore energy transfer. You will investigate the motion of a cart on a ramp, and apply what you learn to the physics of automobile accidents and safety features. A combination of laboratories, investigations, readings, models, debates, role plays, and projects will help you uncover the nature of science and the relevance of physical science to your interests.

You will find that important scientific ideas come up again and again in different activities throughout the book. You will be expected to do more than just memorize these concepts: you will be asked to explain and apply them. In particular, you will improve your decision-making skills by using evidence to weigh outcomes and to decide what you think should be done about the scientific issues facing our society.

How do we know that this is a good way for you to learn? In general, research on science education supports it. In particular, the activities in this book were tested by hundreds of students and their teachers, and then modified on the basis of their feedback. In a sense, this entire book is the result of an investigation: we had people test our ideas, we interpreted the results, and we then revised our ideas! We believe the result will show you that learning more about science is important, enjoyable, and relevant to your life.

SEPUP Staff

ISSUES & PHYSICAL SCIENCE **PROJECT**
Director (2003–2006): Barbara Nagle
Director (2001–2002): Herbert D. Thier

UNIT E AUTHORS
Janet Bellantoni
Daniel Seaver

OTHER CONTRIBUTORS
Lee Trampleasure, Kate Haber, Manisha Hariani, Vana James, Barbara
Nagle, Mike Reeske

CONTENT AND SCIENTIFIC REVIEW
Tim Erickson, Epistemological Engineering, Oakland, California

PRODUCTION
Production Coordinator: Ayse Frosina
SEPUP Publications Coordinator: Miriam Shein
Design and Composition: Seventeenth Street Studios
Photo Research: Seventeenth Street Studios
Editing: Trish Beall
Administrative Assistance: Roberta Smith, Ezequiel Gonzalez, Michelle Mills

Field Test Centers

The classroom is SEPUP's laboratory for development. We are extremely appreciative of the following center directors and teachers who taught the program during the 2004–05 school year. These teachers and their students contributed significantly to improving the course.

BUFFALO, NEW YORK
Kathaleen Burke, *Center Director*
Robert Baxter, Robert Tyrell

CHARLESTON COUNTY, SOUTH CAROLINA
Rodney Moore, *Center Director*
Deborah Bellflower, Liz Milliken, Donna Ouzts, Gail Wallace

LEMON GROVE, CALIFORNIA
Samantha Swann, *Center Director*
Lyn Ann Boulette, Amber Lunde

WINSTON-SALEM/FORSYTH COUNTY, NORTH CAROLINA
Jim Bott, *Center Director*
Kathy Boyer, Jason Felten, Bill Martin

Contents

UNIT E Force and Motion

73 TALKING IT OVER
Choosing a Safe Vehicle   E-4

74 LABORATORY
Measuring Speed   E-7

75 INVESTIGATION
Interpreting Motion Graphs   E-12

76 LABORATORY
Speed and Collisions   E-16

77 LABORATORY
Mass and Collision   E-19

78 PROBLEM SOLVING
Force, Acceleration, and Mass   E-21

79 LABORATORY
Inertia Around a Curve   E-25

80 READING
Newton's Laws of Motion   E-29

81 INVESTIGATION
The Net Force Challenge   E-37

82 LABORATORY
Braking Distance   E-41

83 INVESTIGATION
Coming to a Stop   E-45

84 READING
Decelerating Safely   E-49

85 INVESTIGATION
Crash Testing   E-55

86 MODELING
Investigating Center of Mass   E-58

87 TALKING IT OVER
Fatal Accidents   E-62

88 ROLE PLAY
Safety for All   E-65

Index   E-69

Force and
Motion

E

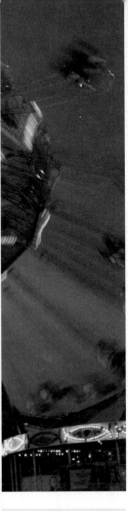

Force and Motion

I can't wait until school is over," Jack said to his friend Uma. "My favorite relative, Aunt Tillie, is visiting. She drives a tour bus and today she is going to pick me up from school in it!"

When Tillie arrived, Jack climbed on board the bus, and sat up front so he could see everything. As Aunt Tillie turned onto a two-lane highway entrance, Jack noticed that there was a car right next to them. The car quickly accelerated past them and got on the highway. This got Jack thinking about how things move.

"Aunt Tillie," he asked, "Why can that car get up to highway speed faster than us? The engine on this bus is so much bigger."

"But that car is a lot smaller than this bus," she answered.

"So, why should that matter?"

"Well, it's physics, Jack," said Aunt Tillie. "It's hard to increase the speed of something big, like this bus. It needs a really big engine to create enough force."

"But the engine of the bus is big. It creates a lot more force than that little car's engine."

"Yes, but since the car is small, it doesn't need as much force to get it up to speed. Its smaller engine can create enough force to make it go faster than the bus.

• • •

How are forces related to motion? How does the size of something affect how it moves?

In this unit, you will learn how forces affect the motion of an object. By examining car collisions, you will also learn how an understanding of motion can improve safety on the road.

VIEW AND REFLECT

Last week, as Noah's dad was driving him to school, they were in a traffic accident. Although no one was hurt, the car is too damaged to drive and it has to be replaced. Noah's parents want to make sure that the next vehicle they buy is very safe. They've narrowed down the choice to two different vehicles that cost about the same. Even though Noah isn't old enough to drive yet, his parents want his opinion and they show him short advertisements for each one:

Vehicle 1

> *RUGGED! STRONG!*
> *Now with more horsepower than any other vehicle in its class. You can safely take five people and all their gear anywhere you want to go. Yes, anywhere!*

Vehicle 2

> *QUICK! RESPONSIVE!*
> *This high-performance sports sedan gives you quick acceleration and precision handling. And it's so roomy that a family of five can travel safely across town or across the country!*

CHALLENGE ⟹ Which vehicle do you think is safer?

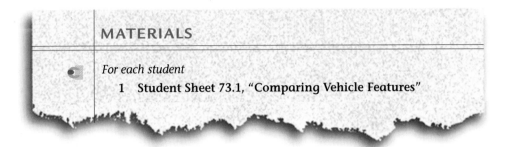

MATERIALS

For each student
    1 **Student Sheet 73.1, "Comparing Vehicle Features"**

PROCEDURE

Part A: Prioritizing Vehicle Features

1. Discuss with your partner what you consider to be important features in a family vehicle.

2. In your science notebook:

    a. List the five features that are most important to you.

    b. List the five features that most affect a vehicle's safety.

    c. Circle any features that appear on both lists.

3. Ask your teacher for a copy of Student Sheet 73.1, "Comparing Vehicle Features." On it:

    a. Draw a star to the left of the names of the five features that are *most* important to you.

    b. Draw an "X" to the left of the names of the five features that are *least* important to you.

4. Answer Analysis Questions 1–2.

Part B: Analyzing Vehicle Features for Safety

5. For each feature listed on Student Sheet 73.1, use the "Effect on Safety" column to explain how you think that feature makes the vehicle more or less safe. If you don't think the feature has any effect, explain why not.

6. For each feature listed, compare the data for Vehicles 1 and 2. Circle the number of the vehicle which the data indicates would be safer.

7. Answer Analysis Questions 3–6.

ANALYSIS

1. Compare the features you listed in Step 2 to the features listed on Student Sheet 73.1. How are they:

   a. similar?

   b. different?

2. For each feature on Student Sheet 73.1 that you drew an "X" next to, explain why you decided it was less important.

 3. What factors other than safety do people consider when buying a car?

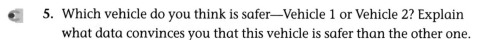 4. Do you think car features can:

   a. reduce damage, injuries, and fatalities in car accidents? Explain.

   b. prevent accidents? Explain.

5. Which vehicle do you think is safer—Vehicle 1 or Vehicle 2? Explain what data convinces you that this vehicle is safer than the other one.

LABORATORY

Although many factors contribute to car accidents, speeding is the most common kind of risky driving. Unsafe speed is involved in about 20% of fatal car accidents in the United States.

Speed is the distance an object travels in a certain amount of time. For example, a car that travels a distance of 80 kilometers in one hour has a speed of 80 kilometers per hour. Any object's speed can be calculated by dividing the distance traveled by the time taken, as shown in the equation:

$$\text{speed} = \frac{\text{distance}}{\text{time}}$$

People use many different units to describe speed. These include miles per hour (MPH), kilometers per hour (kph or km/h), and meters per second (m/s).

CHALLENGE → **How can you measure the speed of a moving cart?**

This car speedometer shows speed in miles per hour and in kilometers per hour. Kilometers per hour is the speed unit commonly used in other countries.

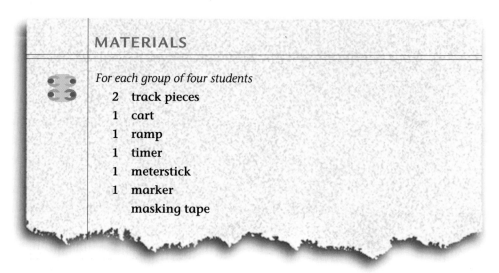

MATERIALS

For each group of four students

2 track pieces
1 cart
1 ramp
1 timer
1 meterstick
1 marker
masking tape

PROCEDURE

Part A: Measuring Time and Distance

1. Set up the ramp and track as shown below.

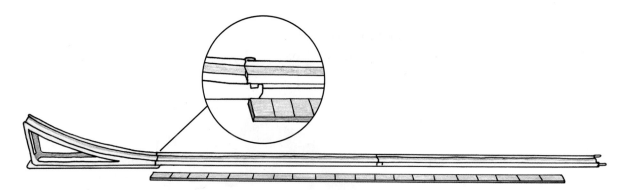

2. Use the meterstick, masking tape, and marker to measure and mark the beginning and end of the first 100 cm of the level part of the track. Make sure to place the tape next to the track instead of directly on the track.

The fastest track cyclists can travel a 4000 meter (2.5 mile) track in just under 4 minutes.

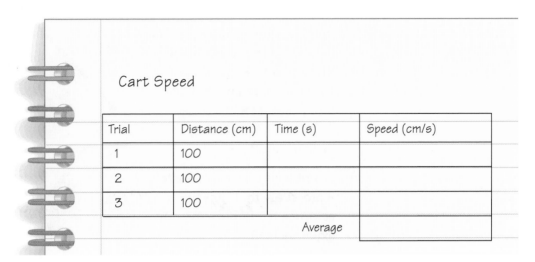

Cart Speed

Trial	Distance (cm)	Time (s)	Speed (cm/s)
1	100		
2	100		
3	100		
		Average	

3. In your science notebook, make a table like the one above.

4. Hold the cart so that its rear axle is at Notch A on the ramp.

5. Release the cart, and start the stopwatch when the rear wheels of the cart travels over the beginning of the level track. Time how long it takes until the rear wheels travel to the 100 cm mark. Record the time in your table in the Trial 1 row.

6. Repeat Steps 4–5 two more times. Use the Trial 2 and 3 rows to record your data.

7. Use the equation below to calculate the speed of the cart for each trial:

$$\text{speed} = \frac{\text{distance}}{\text{time}}$$

8. Calculate the average of the three trials. Record the average of the speeds in your table.

Part B: The Effect of Release Height

9. Imagine what would happen to the cart speed if you changed the release height of the cart. In your science notebook, write how releasing it at a lesser height would affect its speed. Explain.

10. To test your prediction, write a procedure that uses the equipment you have already experimented with.

    Hint: Your plan should take into account that the cart might not always travel 100 cm before coming to a stop.

11. Prepare a data table for recording your measurements.

12. Show your plans to your teacher.

13. Carry out your experiment and record your data.

ANALYSIS

1. According to your data from Part A, what is the speed of the cart?

2. According to your data from Part B, what is the effect of release height on speed?

3. List some common units for speed. Why are there so many different units?

4. What part(s) of your experimental design in Part B:

    a. increased your confidence in the results?

    b. decreased your confidence in the results?

5. What is a car's speed in m/s if it travels:

    a. 5 meters in 0.1 seconds?

    b. 5 meters in 0.2 seconds?

    c. 10 meters in 0.2 seconds?

6. **Reflection:** Why do you think speeding is a factor in about 20% of fatal car accidents?

EXTENSION 1

Post your results on the *Issues and Physical Science* page of the SEPUP website, and compare your data set to that of students in other classes.

EXTENSION 2

If the speed limit is 60 MPH, could the police give a speeding ticket to any of the drivers of the cars in Analysis Question 5?

Hint: 1,000 m = 1 km = 0.62 miles

A radar gun uses sound waves to measure how far a car moves in a short amount of time. It quickly calculates the speed and displays it for the user.

INVESTIGATION

In the previous activity, you calculated the speed of a cart during its trip on a track. Sometimes, however, the speed of an object changes during a trip. For example, the driver of a car often changes the speed of the car because of traffic or road conditions. When the speed of an object changes over the course of a trip, a motion graph is useful because it shows the speed during all parts of the trip.

Teasha and Josh live next door to each other at the end of a long straight road that goes directly to their school. They live four miles from the school, and their parents drive them there in the mornings.

CHALLENGE → **How can you use a graph to describe motion?**

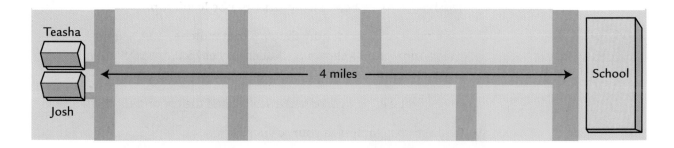

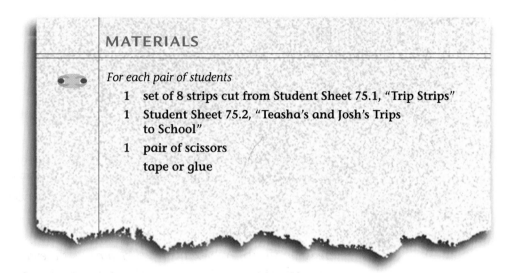

MATERIALS

For each pair of students

1 set of 8 strips cut from Student Sheet 75.1, "Trip Strips"

1 Student Sheet 75.2, "Teasha's and Josh's Trips to School"

1 pair of scissors

tape or glue

PROCEDURE

1. Cut apart the 8 trip strips along the dotted lines.

2. Read the trip strips. Each strip represents a story or one or more pieces of a story for two stories mixed together. Some of the strips describe Teasha's trip to school. The others describe Josh's trip.

3. With your partner, identify the strip that matches each segment of the two motion graphs shown on Student Sheet 75.2, "Teasha's and Josh's Trips to School."

4. Glue or tape each strip onto the segment of the graph that it describes.

5. Explain your choices in your science notebook.

ANALYSIS

1. Identify a place on each graph where the slope of the line changes. What does a change in the slope of a motion graph indicate?

2. Which student—Teasha or Josh—started out faster? Explain how you know this.

3. How far into the trip did Josh turn around? Describe what the graph looks like at this point in the trip.

4. Look at the motion graphs shown below. Match the descriptions here to the correct graphs:

   a. A car moving at a constant speed stops and then moves in the opposite direction at the same speed.

   b. A car moving at a constant speed stops and then moves faster in the same direction.

   c. A car moving at a constant speed changes to a higher constant speed.

   d. A car moving at a constant speed changes to a lower constant speed.

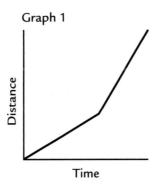

Graph 1

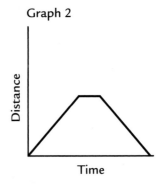

Graph 2

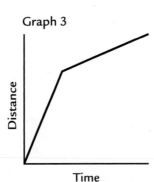

Graph 3

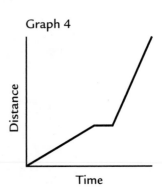

Graph 4

5. A car that accelerates (ak-SELL-ur-ates) is one that changes speed and/or direction. Which graph below shows a car continually accelerating? Explain how the shape of the graph shows this.

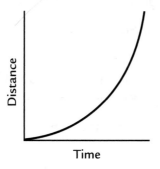

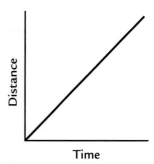

EXTENSION

Create one or more new character(s) also riding in cars for the scenario of this activity. For each character, make up another set of trip strips and a motion graph to go with them.

LABORATORY

In a car accident, both the speed of the car and the speed of the object it hits are likely to change. These changes happen because of forces that occur when any moving object collides (kuh-LYDZ) with another object. A force is a push or pull, and it is what changes the motion of an object. The change in an object's motion depends on two factors: the size of the force and the length of time the force is applied. In many car crashes, the length of time of the actual collision is very short.

CHALLENGE ⟶ **Does vehicle speed affect the forces involved in a collision?**

The force with which these cars hit is large, but the time it took to collide was short.

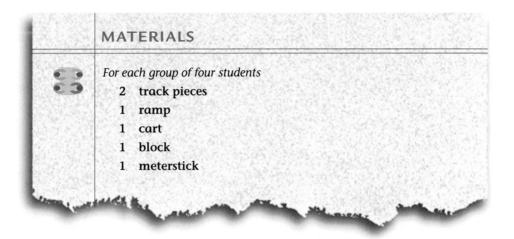

MATERIALS

For each group of four students

2 track pieces
1 ramp
1 cart
1 block
1 meterstick

PROCEDURE

1. In your science notebook, make a table like the one below.

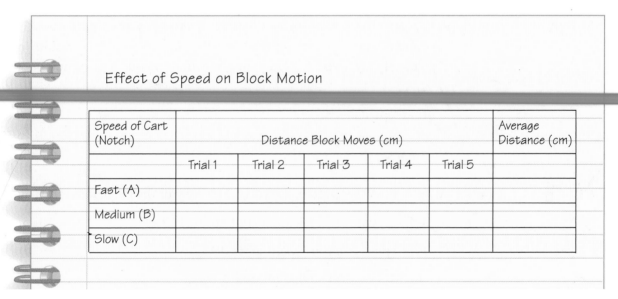

Effect of Speed on Block Motion

Speed of Cart (Notch)	Distance Block Moves (cm)					Average Distance (cm)
	Trial 1	Trial 2	Trial 3	Trial 4	Trial 5	
Fast (A)						
Medium (B)						
Slow (C)						

2. Set up the ramp and track as you did in Activity 74, "Measuring Speed" but without the 100 cm marking.

3. Mark the track 5 cm from the bottom edge of the ramp, and place the block there, as shown below.

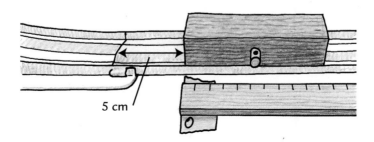

5 cm

4. Hold the cart so that its rear axle is at Notch A on the ramp. As you learned in Activity 74, releasing the cart from Notch A results in the fastest cart speed.

5. Release the cart, and observe what happens. Measure the distance that the block moved down the track. Record the data as Trial 1 in your table.

6. Repeat Steps 3–5 four more times, and record the data as Trials 2–5.

7. Calculate the average distance the block moved and record this in your data table.

8. Predict what you think will happen to the block if the cart starts from Notch B. Remember that releasing the cart from Notch B results in a medium cart speed. Record your prediction in your science notebook.

9. Hold the cart so the rear axle of the vehicle is at Notch B on the ramp instead of Notch A, and repeat Steps 3–7.

10. Predict what you think will happen to the block if the cart starts from Notch C. Remember that releasing the cart from Notch C results in the slowest cart speed. Record your prediction in your science notebook.

11. Hold the cart so the rear axle of the cart is at Notch C on the ramp, and repeat Steps 3–7.

ANALYSIS

1. How does the speed of the cart affect how far the block moves?

2. Why do you think release height has this effect?

3. What part(s) of the experiment's design:

   a. increase your confidence in the data?

   b. decrease your confidence in the data?

4. When a car crashes, do you think its speed can make a difference in the amount of damage done? Explain, using evidence from this investigation.

LABORATORY

In the previous activity you investigated how the speed of the cart affects a collision. In this activity, you will investigate whether the mass of the cart affects the force it can apply during a collision. Mass describes the amount of matter in an object. For example, a small car has less mass than a big truck.

CHALLENGE ⟶ **Does the mass of an object affect the force it applies during a collision?**

What are the properties of this hammer that give it the potential to apply a lot of force?

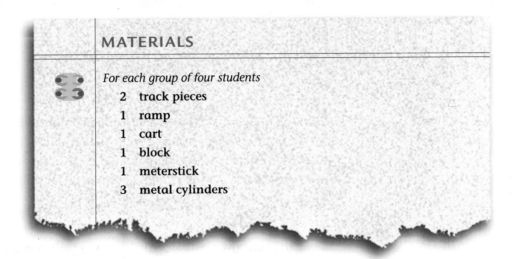

MATERIALS

For each group of four students

2 track pieces
1 ramp
1 cart
1 block
1 meterstick
3 metal cylinders

PROCEDURE

1. Write down your prediction of how changing the mass of the cart will affect a collision between the cart and a wooden block.

2. Write out a materials list and procedure for an experiment to test your prediction.

3. Prepare a data table for recording your measurements.

4. Show your plans to your teacher and get the necessary equipment.

5. Carry out your experiment and record your data.

ANALYSIS

1. Did the mass of the cart affect the collision? Explain how you know this.

2. Why do you think mass did or did not have the effect you predicted?

3. What part(s) of the experimental design:

   a. increase your confidence in the data?

   b. decrease your confidence in the data?

4. If your car were in a collision, would you rather be hit by Vehicle 1 (2,027 kg) or Vehicle 2 (1,415 kg) from Activity 73? Explain.

PROBLEM SOLVING

In the previous activities, you learned about force, mass, and changes in motion. In this activity, you will investigate the precise relationship between the mass of an object, the force applied to it, and the object's acceleration.

You also learned earlier that scientists measure speed in m/s (meters per second), and they measure mass in kg (kilograms). In this activity, you will need to know the standard international (SI) units used to measure force and acceleration. Acceleration is the change in speed (measured in meters per second) divided by time (measured in seconds), and so the unit for acceleration is meters per second per second (m/s·s or m/s^2). Force is measured in newtons (N). This unit is named after Sir Isaac Newton, a scientist who studied forces and motion.

CHALLENGE ➡ **What is the mathematical relationship between force, acceleration, and mass?**

The golf ball in the photo on the right will have a greater change in motion because it is hit with a greater force.

MATERIALS

For each student
graph paper

PROCEDURE

Part A: Graphing the Variables

1. The table below shows precise measurements from an experiment in which a force is applied to pull a block along a frictionless track.

Experiment 1		
Force (N)	Mass of Block (kg)	Acceleration of Block (m/sec²)
4.0	2.0	2.0
2.0	2.0	1.0
20.0	2.0	10.0
10.0	2.0	5.0

2. Use the Experiment 1 data to make a graph of the relationship between acceleration and force. Title the graph, "Acceleration vs. Force." Label the graphed line "Experiment 1."

   Hint: Put the data for acceleration on the x-axis and the data for force on the y-axis.

3. Answer Analysis Question 1.

Part B: Finding the Equation

4. Use the Experiment 1 data to determine a mathematical equation that shows the exact relationship between mass (m), force (F), and acceleration (a). Record the relationship in your science notebook.

   Hint: Try adding, subtracting, multiplying, and dividing two of the measurements to see if you get the third.

Part C: Double-checking the Equation

5. The data table below shows measurements from Experiment 2. See whether your equation works for this set of data.

   • If it does, go on to Step 6.

   • If it doesn't, find a different equation that does work for both experiments.

Experiment 2		
Force (N)	Mass of Block (kg)	Acceleration of Block (m/sec²)
4.0	4.0	1.0
2.0	4.0	0.5
20.0	4.0	5.0
10.0	4.0	2.5

6. Using the same graph you made in Step 2, plot the Experiment 2 data. Label the second line "Experiment 2."

ANALYSIS

1. Look at your graphed line for Experiment 1. Explain why it does or does not indicate that there is a relationship between force and acceleration.

2. Compare the two lines, "Experiment 1" and "Experiment 2" on your graph. Identify and explain:

   a. any similarities.

   b. any differences.

How does the acceleration of the dogs affect the force on the sled?

3. In your science notebook, make a table like the one below. Use your equation for force, mass, and acceleration to find the missing values.

Experiment 3

Force (N)	Mass of Block (kg)	Acceleration of Block (m/sec²)
	5	5
	2	10
10		2
50	10	
100		25
1,000	40	

4. In the first activity, Vehicle 2 has a greater acceleration than Vehicle 1, but has a less forceful engine. How can this be? Explain in terms of your equation.

5. One Newton of force is the same as 1 kg 3 1 m/s². Explain how this unit of measurement is appropriate for your equation.

LABORATORY

It takes more force, and often more time and distance, for a heavier car to stop or swerve to avoid an accident. A heavier car has more inertia than a lighter car. **Inertia** (in-UR-sha) is the resistance of an object to changes in its motion. In other words, inertia describes the tendency of an object to continue moving at the same speed and in the same direction, such as a train traveling in a straight line at 60 MPH. Continuing at the "same speed" may mean a speed of 0 m/s, or continuing to not move.

The more mass an object has, the more inertia it has, and the greater the force it takes to change its motion. Understanding inertia helps us understand and predict what a vehicle will do when forces are applied or removed.

CHALLENGE ⟹ **How does inertia affect how an object moves?**

The bigger ship has more inertia than the small boat.

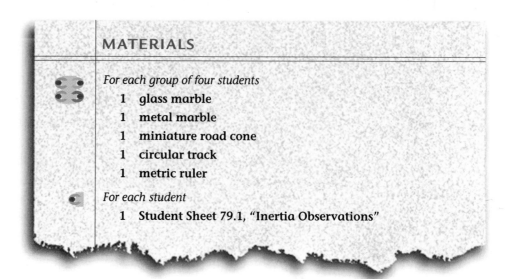

MATERIALS

For each group of four students

1 glass marble
1 metal marble
1 miniature road cone
1 circular track
1 metric ruler

For each student

1 Student Sheet 79.1, "Inertia Observations"

PROCEDURE

Part A: High Mass Marble

1. Set up the circular track as shown below, and make sure it is placed where everyone in your group can easily view it.

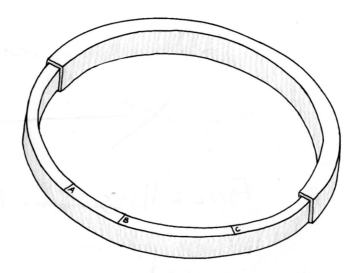

2. Practice sending the metal marble counterclockwise around the inside of the circular track with enough speed to make it go around two or three times before stopping.

   Hint: You may need to hold the track still while the marble is traveling around the track.

3. Set the opening to "A."

4. Discuss with your group where you predict the metal marble will roll once it has gone around the circular track and travels out through the opening.

5. Place the miniature road cone on the table to mark the position of your prediction from Step 4.

6. On Student Sheet 79.1, "Inertia Observations," show the path you predicted by drawing a series of three "x"s, each about 1 cm apart in the "Position A" diagram.

7. Using the same speed you practiced in Step 2, send the metal marble around the inside of the circular track and observe the path it takes after it travels out through the opening.

8. Repeat step 7 several times until the members of your group agree on the most common path of the marble.

9. Draw a solid line on the "Position A" diagram to record the most common path of the marble.

10. Discuss with your group why the marble took that path. Record your ideas next to the diagram.

11. Repeat Steps 3–10 for the Position B and C openings in the circular track.

Part B: Low Mass Marble

12. Repeat Steps 1–11 with the glass marble instead of the metal marble.

In which direction does the passengers' inertia carry them?

ANALYSIS

1. Describe the changes in direction and speed of the marbles when they traveled:

    a inside the circular track.

    b. outside the circular track.

2. Describe any changes in the path of the marble that occurred when you changed:

    a. the opening position of the circular track.

    b. the mass of the marble.

3. Imagine that a car is approaching a curve in the road when it suddenly loses its steering and brakes. The area is flat and there is no guardrail on the road.

    a. Copy the diagram below in your science notebook. Then draw a line showing the car's path when it loses its steering and brakes.

    b. Explain why the car will take that path.

    c. How would your answer change if the car had more mass? Explain.

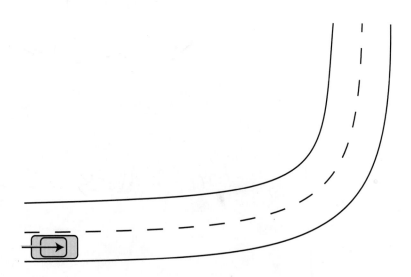

READING

saac Newton was a British scientist whose accomplishments included important discoveries about light, motion, and gravity. You may have heard the legend about how he "discovered" gravity when he was sitting under an apple tree and an apple fell on his head. He didn't really discover gravity, but he did realize that there is a gravitational force that constantly pulls objects toward the center of Earth. This force makes objects fall toward Earth if no other force is there to hold them up.

CHALLENGE

What relationships between force and motion did Newton discover?

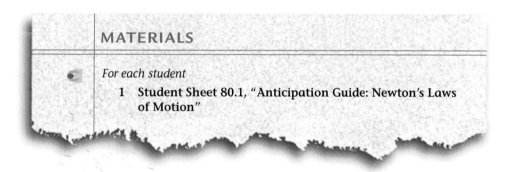

MATERIALS

For each student

1 **Student Sheet 80.1, "Anticipation Guide: Newton's Laws of Motion"**

This image of Isaac Newton appears in one of his books, published in the 1600s.

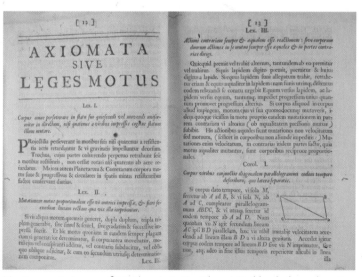

Newton wrote Laws of Motion *in Latin. The original book shown here is in the collection of the Library of Congress in Washington, D.C.*

READING

Use Student Sheet 80.1, "Anticipation Guide: Newton's Laws of Motion," to prepare you for the following reading.

Force and Motion

People have probably always observed objects in motion and have made objects move around. For many centuries, scientists thought they knew everything about this. However, the Italian scientist Galileo Galilei, who lived from 1564 to 1642, began to think about motion in a new way. Isaac Newton, who was born the year Galileo died, built upon his discoveries and developed three laws. Newton's laws were revolutionary, as they seemed to go against everyday experience and observation. Today, parts of Newton's three laws are still the basis for understanding motion.

Newton's First Law: The Law of Inertia

Newton's first law, also known as the Law of Inertia, can be difficult to fully understand. It describes an object's resistance to changing its motion and its tendency to keep doing whatever it is doing. A change in motion can be a change in an object's speed, direction, or both. For example, a car that speeds up to pass another car, or that turns a corner is changing its motion. Newton's first law states that an object's motion cannot change unless a force acts on the object. In other words, it takes a force to overcome an object's inertia and to make the object go faster, slower, or change direction.

STOPPING TO THINK 1

Which has more inertia: a heavy ball or a light ball rolling at the same speed in the same direction? Think about which one is more resistant to a change in motion.

Since you may already know that it takes a force to change motion, you might be wondering, "What's so hard to understand about Newton's first law?" The difficulty is that this law also says that no force is needed to keep something moving. According to Newton's first law, if something is moving at a certain speed, it will keep on moving at that speed forever. It will not slow down and stop unless something pulls or pushes on it. The idea also applies to an object that is not moving. It will remain motionless until a force acts on it.

Newton's first law seems to contradict everyday experience. You've seen for yourself that when you kick, throw, or bat a ball along the ground it eventually stops by itself. And when you ride a sled or a scooter down a hill, you don't keep going forever; you slow down and stop. How can Newton's first law be correct?

Friction

What is not stated in Newton's first law, but plays an important role in motion, is the idea of **friction** (FRICK-shun). Friction is a force that exists at the boundary between any two pieces of matter that are in contact with each other. Friction is a force that opposes the motion of an object. For example, the friction between a rolling ball and the ground causes the ball to slow down and stop rolling. Friction between a sliding sled and snow causes the sled to slow down and stop sliding. Here on the earth, where there is friction everywhere, a force must be applied to an object in order to keep it moving.

If there were no friction, the inertia of a moving object would keep it moving the same way forever or until a force changes its motion. In outer

There is less friction between the puck and the ice (left) than there is between the ball and the rougher grass (right).

space, which has no ground, water, or air to create friction, an object would keep moving forever at the same speed and in the same direction. This explains why the moons and the planets and other space objects have been moving for billions of years and will keep moving for billions more!

STOPPING TO THINK 2

What would happen to a baseball if you could throw it in outer space? Explain in terms of inertia and friction.

To keep a car moving, its engine has to keep pushing it to overcome the friction in several places, such as the road and the tires, and the windshield and the air. Many features on vehicles are designed to reduce friction as much as possible. Shapes are streamlined to reduce air friction, and oil and grease reduce friction between moving parts. If there is less friction to overcome, the engine doesn't need to apply as much force. Other vehicle features are designed to increase friction. Tires need to have friction so that they can "grab" the road and brakes need a lot of friction to make the wheels stop turning.

The bobsled and its passengers try to reduce friction. Snow tires increase friction to bring the wheels to a stop.

As the train travels at constant speed, the engine must produce enough force to equal the friction caused by the air and the wheels on the track.

Balanced Forces

To keep an object moving at a constant speed in the presence of frictional force, a force needs to be applied that is equal in size to, but in the opposite direction of, the frictional force. This applied force balances the force of friction so that the combined force acting on the object, or the **net force**, is zero (0). The engine of a car that is moving at a constant speed is applying a force exactly equal to the frictional forces that are pushing against it. When the net force is zero, there are balanced forces and there is no change in motion, just as Newton's first law states.

STOPPING TO THINK 3

A car travels along a straight road at a steady 40 MPH. Are the forces on the car balanced or unbalanced? Explain.

Newton's Second Law:
The Relationship Between Force, Mass, and Acceleration

Unlike the first law, Newton's second law is confirmed by our everyday experiences and is easier to understand. It states that:

1. To equally change the motion of two objects of different mass, more force must be applied to the more massive object. For example, when you add weight to a wagon, you have to push it harder to speed it up because it has more inertia.

2. The bigger the force that is applied to an object, the greater the resulting acceleration. For example, if you give a soccer ball a soft tap with your foot (a small force over a short period of time) it doesn't speed up much. If you give it a hard kick (a larger force over an equally short period of time) it speeds up more.

Newton summed up these ideas with a single equation that shows the the net force (F) needed to accelerate (a) any mass (m):

$$F = ma$$

STOPPING TO THINK 4

Can a light object that was hit with a small force accelerate as rapidly as a heavier object hit with a big force? Why or why not?

Unbalanced Forces

Newton's second law describes the change in motion that is a result of unbalanced forces. If net force on an object is not zero, the forces are unbalanced and the object accelerates. Even a tiny force will cause an object to speed up if it is not balanced by another force. In a frictionless world, an object that has a continually applied force would speed up until it is traveling as fast as it possibly can.

Race horses accelerate out of the starting gate.

Newton's Third Law: Action-Reaction with Two Objects

Newton was the first one to notice that it is impossible to have a single force. Forces always happen in pairs. Newton's third law, also know as the Law of Action-Reaction explains how a pair of forces work. It states that when one object applies a force on a second object, the second object applies the same size force in the opposite direction, and for the same amount of time, on the first object. Another way to think about this is that when one object pushes or pulls on another object the other object will always push or pull back with the same force. An example Newton used was that if you push a rock with your hand, the rock pushes back on your hand. Another example is a launching rocket. It is propelled because, at the same time as the rocket is pushing the gases down, the force of the gases is pushing the rocket up.

The force of the gases pushes downward at the same time that the gases push the rocket upwards.

It may seem that the third law contradicts the second law. If there are always equal and opposite forces, how can there ever be an unbalanced force? In the second law, Newton talks about the net force acting on a single object. The opposing forces in Newton's third law are two forces acting on a pair of different objects. When the second law is used to describe motion, the action-reaction forces are still there, but they are often ignored since they are equal and opposite.

STOPPING TO THINK 5

If you hold a backpack in your hand, the force of gravity pulls it downward. What force keeps it from falling to the ground?

ANALYSIS

1. Spaceships that travel millions of miles into outer space use very little fuel. How can they go so far on so little fuel?

2. Use Newton's laws to explain why it is easier to turn a truck when it is empty than when it is carrying a heavy load.

3. An engine can exert a force of 1,000 newtons. How fast can this engine accelerate:

   a. a 1,000-kg car?

   b. a 2,000-kg car?

4. Use Newton's third law to explain why a blown up but untied balloon will fly around the room when you let it go.

5. Motor oil, axle grease, and other lubricants are slippery. Why do you think people spend the money to put these lubricants in their cars?

Imagine a car that is moving at a constant speed in a straight line. The frictional forces that would slow the car down are balanced by the engine force that moves the car forward. The result is a zero (0) net force on the car. According to Newton's second law, the car is not accelerating— it's not speeding up, not slowing down, and not changing direction. An object's acceleration only changes when there is an unbalanced (nonzero) net force acting on it.

CHALLENGE

How can you tell if the forces on an object are balanced or unbalanced?

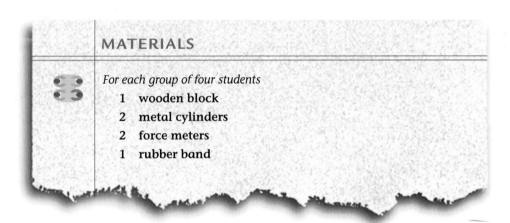

MATERIALS

For each group of four students

1 wooden block
2 metal cylinders
2 force meters
1 rubber band

PROCEDURE

Part A: Balanced Forces

1. Place the block on the table, and hook both force meters to it as shown below.

   Note: Each mark on the force meter is 0.1 N.

2. While *not* moving the block, have one group member pull gently with **1.0 N** on one force meter, while another pulls gently with **1.0 N** on the other force meter.

3. In your science notebook, draw a force diagram of the block, similar to the example below. On your diagram record the forces on the block from Step 2.

Part B: Unbalanced Forces

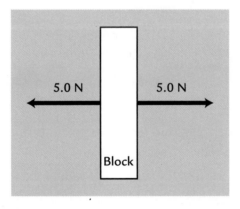

4. Pull gently with **1.5 N** on one force meter, while another group member pulls gently with **1.0 N** on the other force meter. The other two group members should watch the block and observe its motion.

5. Switch roles, and repeat Step 4 until each group member gets to pull the block and observe its motion.

6. Discuss with your group members the motion of the block. In particular, decide if the block was accelerating or not. Record your conclusion in your science notebook.

7. Draw another force diagram of the block in your science notebook. Record the forces from Step 4. Title your diagram "Nonzero Net Force."

Part C: The Challenge

In this part of the activity, your challenge is to decide if the forces on the block are balanced or unbalanced.

8. Unhook one of the force meters. Place two metal cylinders on the block and secure them with the rubber band as shown below.

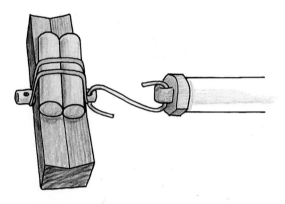

9. Practice pulling gently on the force meter so that the block slides steadily and as slowly as possible.

10. When you can do this well, read the force needed to pull the block slowly and steadily.

11. Switch roles, and repeat Steps 9 and 10 until each group member gets to pull the block and observe its motion.

12. With your group members, discuss the motion of the block. In particular, identify all the forces on the block, and then decide if the block was accelerating or not. Record your conclusion in your science notebook.

13. Draw a force diagram of the block at Step 10. Title your diagram "Zero Net Force" or "Nonzero Net Force," depending on the conclusion of your group.

ANALYSIS

1. Describe an example and draw a force diagram of a situation with:

   a. balanced forces.

   b. unbalanced forces.

2. Imagine that a parked car is hit from the left with 30,000 N of force at the exact same time it is hit from the right with 40,000 N of force.

   a. Draw a force diagram showing the two forces acting on the parked car.

   b. Draw another force diagram showing only the net force on the parked car.

3. The force diagram below shows an object with zero net force, but there is one force missing. What is the missing force? Draw the diagram in your notebook, and complete it by drawing and labeling the missing force.

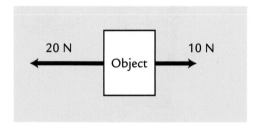

4. Look back at your work from Part A. Could the block in Part A have been moving? Explain.

5. For each situation in a–e below, explain why there is or is not a zero net force acting on the car.

   a. A car is parked on a level parking space.

   b. A traffic light turns green, and a car starts to move.

   c. A car drives steadily at 25 MPH.

   d. A car is slowing down from 30 MPH to 10 MPH.

   e. A car goes around a corner at 10 MPH.

LABORATORY

One very important force frequently used in a car is the force applied by the brakes. Sometimes drivers can avoid an accident by coming to a stop before the accident occurs. The braking distance is the distance the car travels after the driver applies the brakes, until the car comes to a full stop. Other things being equal, the vehicle with the shorter braking distance is safer.

When the brakes of a car are applied, the brake pads push against a metal section of the wheels. The increased friction acting against the wheels' motion slows down the turning of the wheels.

CHALLENGE

How can friction lower the risk of getting into an accident?

The space shuttle Endeavor uses a drag chute when it lands back on earth. The friction between the chute and the air reduces the shuttle braking distance by about 600 meters.

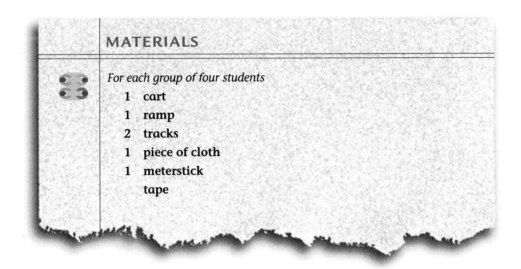

PROCEDURE

1. In your science notebook, make a table like the one below.

Effect of Speed on Braking Distance

Speed of Cart	Braking Distance (cm)			Average Braking Distance (cm)
(Notch)	Trial 1	Trial 2	Trial 3	
Fast (A)				
Medium (B)				
Slow (C)				

2. Set up the equipment as shown below.

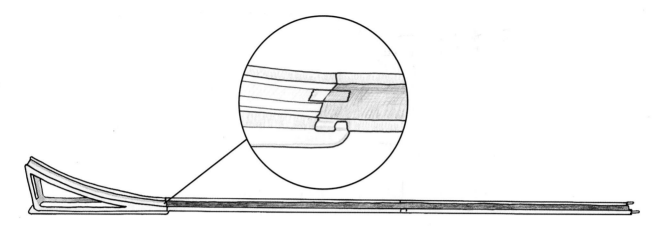

3. Place the cart so that the rear axle is at the high notch, Notch A, on the ramp. As you learned in a previous activity, this release height results in the fastest cart speed.

4. Release the cart, and let it roll to a stop.

5. Measure the distance it rolled along the flat track. Record this distance as Trial 1 in your table.

6. Repeat Steps 3–5 twice, and record the distances as Trial 2 and Trial 3 in your table.

7. Repeat Steps 3–6 with the cart starting at the middle notch, Notch B, on the ramp. This release height results in a medium cart speed. Record your data in your science notebook.

8. Repeat Steps 3–6 with the cart starting at the low notch, Notch C, on the ramp. This release height results in the slowest cart speed. Record your data in your science notebook.

9. Find the average distance the cart traveled for each speed. Record this in the right-hand column of your table.

ANALYSIS

1. In this model of a stopping car:

    a. What does the cloth represent?

    b. List some strengths and weaknesses of this model.

2. What effect does speed have on braking distance? Explain, using evidence from this activity.

3. Does the evidence you gathered in this investigation support the statement below? Explain why or why not, using evidence from your investigation.

    A car moving at 55 MPH needs less distance to stop than an identical car moving at 45 MPH.

4. **Reflection:** Why do you think excessive speed is a factor in about 20% of fatal car accidents?

EXTENSIONS

1. Post your results on the *Issues and Physical Science* page of the SEPUP website, and compare your data sets to those of students in other classes.

INVESTIGATION

A car's braking distance, as you learned in the last activity, is the distance it travels after the brakes are applied until the car comes to a full stop. Braking distance is affected by the speed of the car, the type and quality of brakes, the surfaces of the tires, and the condition of the road.

There is some time that passes, sometimes as long as a few seconds, between the moment a driver realizes there is a problem and the moment his or her foot applies the brakes. This time interval, the driver's **reaction time**, depends primarily on the driver's level of alertness. Drugs, alcohol, sleepiness, and distractions impair alertness, slowing reaction times. The distance the car travels during the reaction time depends on how long it takes the driver to react and how fast the car is traveling.

The **stopping distance** of a car is the total of the distance the car traveled during the reaction time plus the distance traveled while braking.

CHALLENGE ➡ **How does a car's stopping distance change in different situations?**

This distracted driver could be more likely to get in an accident than an alert driver. He has a longer reaction time than does a driver who is not distracted.

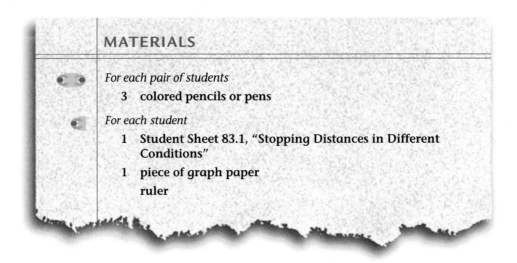

MATERIALS

For each pair of students
   3   colored pencils or pens

For each student
   1   Student Sheet 83.1, "Stopping Distances in Different Conditions"
   1   piece of graph paper
       ruler

PROCEDURE

1. Using the data on Student Sheet 83.1, "Stopping Distances in Different Conditions" and the equation below, calculate the distance a vehicle travels during the driver's reaction time.

   Reaction distance = initial speed × reaction time

   Record your calculations in the "Reaction Distance" column in the three tables.

2. Using the equation below, calculate the vehicle's total stopping distance.

   Stopping distance = reaction distance + braking distance

   Record your calculations in the "Stopping Distance" column of your student sheet.

3. Make a graph of stopping distance (y-axis) versus driving speed (x-axis). Use three different-colored pencils to plot three data sets on the same graph:

   • Plot the points for an alert driver on a slippery road. Label this line "Alert Driver, Slippery Road."

   • Plot the points for an alert driver on a dry road. Label this line "Alert Driver, Dry Road."

   • Plot the points for a distracted driver on a dry road. Label this line "Distracted Driver, Dry Road."

ANALYSIS

1. Why does stopping distance depend on road conditions?

2. What might cause:

    a. slippery road conditions?

    b. driver distractions?

3. In which of the three driving situations (alert and dry, alert and slippery, distracted and dry) does it take:

    a. the least distance to stop? Explain using evidence.

    b. the most distance to stop? Explain using evidence.

4. You are alertly driving a car at 40 MPH (18 m/s). You come around a bend and see a tree that has fallen across the road 50 meters away. Will you be able to stop before you hit the tree:

    a. on a dry road? Show your evidence.

    b. on a wet road? Show your evidence.

5. Would your answers to Analysis Question 4 change:

    a. If something were distracting you as you came around the bend? Explain.

    b. If you were driving 20 MPH instead of 40 MPH? Explain.

6. Your friend says that when a car goes twice as fast, the braking distance doubles. Do you agree or disagree? Use evidence from this investigation to support your ideas.

7. Create a concept map using the following terms:

stopping distance	tires	alertness
reaction distance	brakes	distance
road surface	speed	distraction
braking distance	time	friction

EXTENSION

The table below shows the stopping distances for a distracted driver on a slippery road. Using the graph you made in this activity, plot this data on your graph. Label the line, "Distracted Driver, Slippery Road."

Stopping Distance: Distracted Driver on Slippery Road	
Initial Speed (m/s)	**Stopping Distance (meters)**
5	17
9	40
18	108
27	203
36	326

READING

When a car crashes into something, the driver's and passengers' inertia keeps them moving forward until something stops their motion. Stopping or slowing motion is called **deceleration.** How a person in a car decelerates often determines the seriousness of that person's injuries. Most injuries and deaths occur when internal body parts, such as bones or brains, are decelerated very quickly by a large force.

CHALLENGE ➡ **How can a person's deceleration be controlled during a collision?**

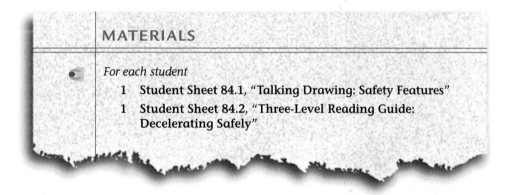

MATERIALS

For each student

1   Student Sheet 84.1, "Talking Drawing: Safety Features"
1   Student Sheet 84.2, "Three-Level Reading Guide: Decelerating Safely"

READING

Use Student Sheet 84.1, "Talking Drawing: Safety Features" and Student Sheet 84.2, "Three-Level Reading Guide: Decelerating Safely" to prepare yourself for the following reading.

Safety Features

To design safer cars, it is important to understand friction, forces, and deceleration. Many safety features help reduce the speed before impact, and other features help protect passengers during a collision. Automobile safety engineers use their knowledge of forces and motion to develop, and continue to improve, many safety features that help avoid accidents or reduce injuries in accidents.

Before the Accident

Driving on a worn-out tire is dangerous because there isn't enough friction between it and the road.

Two of the most important safety features of a car are its brakes and tires. Good tires and brakes help to avoid accidents by using friction to decelerate a car quickly, yet in a controlled way.

The friction between the tires and the road affects braking distance. The amount of this friction depends mostly on the contact area between the tire and the road, the material and tread design of the tire, the type and condition of the road surface, and the temperature of the tire. All new tires are rated for various aspects of safety.

The disc brakes commonly used on cars, like bicycle brakes, work because brake pads squeeze against the two sides of a rotating wheel. The friction between the brake pads and the wheel slows the rotation of the wheels. The larger the surface area of the brake pads, the more friction and, therefore, the greater the braking power. More braking power, however, is not always better.

When a car's brakes clamp down so tightly that they "lock" the wheels, the tires stop rolling and begin to slide on the road. When this happens, the car skids, and the driver can lose control. In this situation there is actually less friction between the tires and the road than when the tires roll. To bring the car to a stop as quickly as possible, friction between the tires and road needs to be maximized. Antilock brake systems (sometimes referred to as

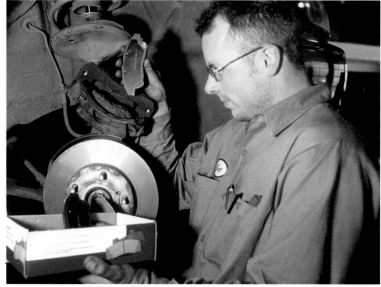

A bicycle brake, above, uses friction between the brake pads and the wheel rim to stop or slow down. In the photo on the right, a mechanic inspects a brake. If the parts become too worn, they won't generate enough friction to stop the car quickly.

ABS) automatically engage and release the brakes many times per second. During the moments when the brakes are released, the tires stop skidding and briefly roll. The overall amount of friction during the pulsing of the ABS brake is higher than if the tires were simply skidding. By maximizing the friction between the tire and the road, antilock brakes help a vehicle stop more quickly and with more control.

During the Accident

When a vehicle is moving, everything inside it, including the passengers, is moving at the same speed as the vehicle, as shown on the left. When a vehicle collides with a solid object, the car stops quickly, but the inertia of the passengers keeps them moving forward until a force changes their motion and slows them down, as shown on the right. If that force is from the steering wheel, dashboard, or windshield, the injuries are often very serious.

The stopping time of a seat-belted passenger may be up to ten times slower than the stopping time for the car.

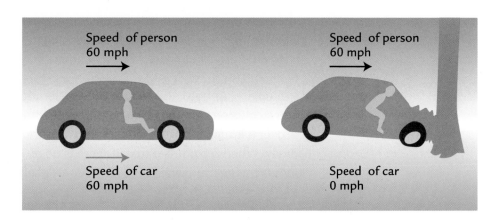

Speed of person
60 mph

Speed of person
60 mph

Speed of car
60 mph

Speed of car
0 mph

Seat belts are designed to reduce the force that a passenger experiences. To reduce the force, seat belts increase the amount of time that it takes to decelerate the passenger. If it takes longer to come to a stop, the deceleration has been reduced. According to Newton's second law, a reduced acceleration (or in this case, deceleration) results in a reduced force:

$$F = ma \qquad\qquad F = ma$$

Smaller deceleration (a) results in a smaller force (F)   Larger deceleration (a) results in a larger force (F)

For example, a car that hits a tree may take about 0.01 seconds from the moment of impact until it comes to a full stop. Without a seatbelt it may take the same amount of time for the driver to also stop. If the driver is wearing a seatbelt, the seatbelt will slow her or him down to a complete stop closer to 0.1 seconds. These time intervals may both seem very fast, but the passenger has taken 10 times longer to come to a stop than the car. This can reduce the maximum force between the seatbelt and the passenger to 1/10 that of the force between the car and the tree. If the driver is not wearing a seatbelt, he or she is likely to be decelerated with a force close to that applied to the car by the tree.

Stopping time for car is 0.01 seconds

Stopping time for seat belted person is 0.1 seconds

Like seatbelts, air bags also reduce the deceleration a person experiences during a collision. Air bags also help by spreading out the deceleration force over a large area. This reduces the pressure, or force per unit area, on the body. When a car hits a tree, if there is no air bag and the driver's forehead hits the steering wheel, the entire force needed to decelerate the driver

is applied to the forehead. This pressure could be great enough to break the skull. With an air bag, the same force is needed to decelerate the driver, but it is spread out evenly over the larger area of the driver's body—head, arms, shoulders, and chest—that hit the air bag. The pressure on any one part is much lower and much less likely to cause injuries. Seatbelts also reduce the pressure on the body by distributing force over the belt, but they have a smaller effect than air bags.

Other Safety Features

A well designed car has a strong occupant compartment, known as the safety cage. The safety cage is important because once it starts to collapse during a collision, the likelihood of injury increases rapidly. Crumple zones are sections in cars that are designed to crumple up when the car collides with something. In a collision, forces are directed to that section of the vehicle instead of being transmitted to the safety cage. Crumple zones increase the damage to the car but reduce the harm done to the occupants. Crumple zones, like air bags and seatbelts, make deceleration more gradual and spread out the area of impact. This can significantly reduce the force felt by the passengers.

Modern steering columns are designed to collapse, as this telescope can.

Cars have not always had as many safety features as today's vehicles. For example, it wasn't until the 1970s that steering wheels were made to be collapsible. Before then, steering wheels were attached to rigid steering columns. If a driver hit the steering wheel with enough force, the rigid steering column could push through the steering wheel and spear the driver. Today's cars have steering columns designed to collapse on impact like a ship captain's telescope. This reduces the chances of being speared. Similarly, headrests, padded dashboards, padded steering wheels, side impact beams, even plastic-covered car keys, and other devices must, by law, be built into new cars.

Safety features in vehicles have come a long way since the automobile was first invented. Although every new generation of cars has better safety features than the previous cars, even the most innovative designs are based on the understanding that passengers are best protected if they decelerate as slowly as possible and if the force is spread over the largest surface possible.

ANALYSIS

1. Choose one of the safety features described in the reading. Use the terms inertia, force, and deceleration to describe how the safety feature helps keep people safe in a collision.

2. As a collision is about to happen, if you had enough time to chose between hitting a large haystack or a telephone pole, which one would you choose to hit? Explain why in terms of force and deceleration.

3. In the accident mentioned in Activity 73, "Choosing a Safe Vehicle," Noah's family car had old tires that were worn down. Explain how this could have contributed to the car accident.

4. **Reflection:** Since the 1920s, the rate of fatalities per billion miles traveled has dropped steadily. However, the rate has been about the same for the past 20 years. Why do you think this is?

INVESTIGATION

Automobile and safety engineers use crash tests to find out how well each kind of car keeps people safe in an accident. In a standard frontal or front-end crash test, the car travels down a track at 35 MPH and smashes into a barrier. In a standard side-impact test, a barrier moving down a track at 31 MPH crashes into the side door of a stationary car. The results of the crash tests show whether the car meets government safety standards and help consumers evaluate and compare the safety of different kinds of cars.

Life-sized human dolls, called crash-test dummies, are used as models for actual passengers. To help predict how badly drivers and passengers could be injured, sensors that measure changes in motion and pressure are placed on various parts of the dummies.

CHALLENGE

Can you design a crash-test dummy?

This high speed photograph of a crash test shows the movement of crash-test dummies placed in the front and back seats.

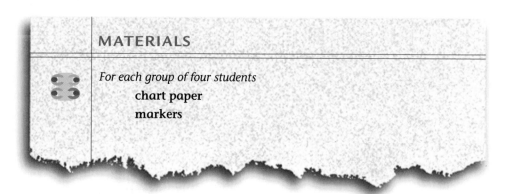

MATERIALS

For each group of four students
chart paper
markers

PROCEDURE

1. Within your group, discuss the following design elements for the crash-test dummy that will be placed in a car's driver's seat. Listen to the ideas of others. If you disagree with others in your group, explain why you disagree. The design considerations are:

   - How should the dummy be like and not like a person?
   - What material(s) should the dummy be made of?
   - How tall and how heavy should the dummy be?
   - What should the sensors measure?
   - Where should the sensors be placed on the dummy?

2. Draw your crash-test dummy design. Include labels and explanations of its different parts.

3. Use an "X" to show the locations of sensors on your drawing. You should show at least five sensors.

4. Prepare a presentation to the class explaining your group's design. Make sure to show all the design elements you discussed in your group, and the scientific reasons for your choices.

ANALYSIS

1. The crash-test dummy that is most often used in frontal crash tests is the Hybrid III dummy. It is 5 feet 9 inches tall, weighs 170 pounds (the size of an average man), and costs about $100,000. What are the advantages and disadvantages of using the Hybrid III in all vehicle crash tests?

EXTENSION

Go to the *Issues and Physical Science* page of the SEPUP website to learn more about vehicle crash testing. Then investigate careers in automotive engineering.

Mass is an important characteristic of an object. Another important characteristic is the object's center of mass. The **center of mass** is the point where the distribution of an object's mass is centered. While mass describes an amount, the center of mass describes a location. For example, a meterstick's center of mass is the point where the mass of the stick is evenly distributed to the left and right ends, to the front and the back, and to one edge and the other. This is where it balances, as shown below.

The center of mass for a vehicle is somewhere inside the vehicle. Vehicles that are tall or ride high off the ground usually have higher centers of mass than vehicles that are less tall and ride closer to the ground. In certain kinds of accidents the vehicle's center of mass can affect what happens to the vehicle and the people inside it.

CHALLENGE → **How does the center of mass affect what happens in a collision?**

The center mass of this meterstick is in the middle.

The center mass of the ruler and eraser is toward one end of the meterstick.

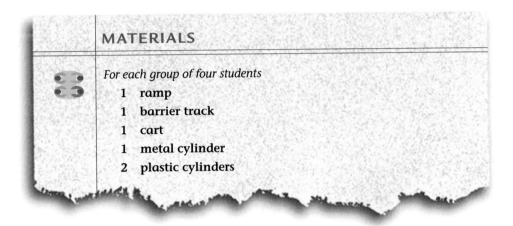

MATERIALS

For each group of four students
1 ramp
1 barrier track
1 cart
1 metal cylinder
2 plastic cylinders

PROCEDURE

1. Attach the barrier track to the ramp.

2. In your science notebook, make a table like the one below.

Center of Mass and Collisions

Mass	Observations	Stability Ranking
Empty Cart		
Loaded Cart, Low Center of Mass		
Loaded Cart, High Center of Mass		

3. While holding the ramp in place, hold the cart so its rear axle is at Notch A of the ramp. Observe what happens when you release the cart and it hits the barrier.

4. Repeat Step 3 several times, and observe what the cart tends to do when it hits the barrier. Record your observations in your table.

5. Place all the cylinders in the cart with the metal one on the bottom. This loaded cart has a low center of mass.

6. With your group, predict what will happen when this loaded cart hits the barrier. Record your prediction in your science notebook.

7. Repeat Steps 3 and 4 using the loaded cart.

8. Now, place all the cylinders in the cart so that the metal one is at the top. This reloaded cart has a high center of mass.

9. With your group, predict what will happen when this reloaded cart hits the barrier. Record your prediction in your science notebook.

10. Repeat Steps 3 and 4 for the reloaded cart.

11. Discuss the results with your group, and compare what happened to the carts when they hit the barrier. In your table, rank with a 1, 2, or 3 the stability of each type of cart: 1 for the most stable cart, and 3 for the least stable cart.

ANALYSIS

1. How did you rank the stability of the carts with three different centers of mass? Describe the observations that determined your ranking.

2. How did a higher center of mass affect the cart's motion after it hit the barrier?

3. Imagine three identical barrels, one empty, one half-full of water, and one full of water. Make a sketch of the barrels in your science notebook, like the ones below.

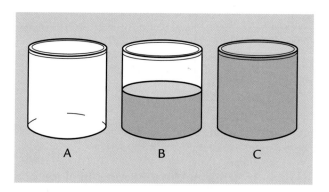

a. Place an "X" on each barrel to show the approximate location of its center of mass.

b. Label the barrel that has the most mass "most mass."

c. Label the barrel with the lowest center of mass "lowest center of mass." Explain why the center of mass is located there.

d. Label the barrel that is easiest to tip over "least stable." Then explain why that barrel is the least stable.

4. Your friend's parents want to haul some lumber in their station wagon. His parents are not sure whether to put the lumber in the wagon or tie it on the roof rack. What advice do you give them? Explain in terms of center of mass.

5. Why do think pick-ups and SUVs tend to roll over more often than passenger cars of similar mass? Explain in terms of center of mass.

EXTENSION

Design an experiment to determine how the cart's speed affects the motion of the cart after it hits the barrier.

TALKING IT OVER

There are many types of vehicles and even more types of accidents. Unfortunately, people are hurt or killed in car accidents every day. Many accidents are caused by driver error, road conditions, vehicle design, or any combination of those. Even when vehicle design is not the cause of an accident, it can contribute to the severity of the damage.

The design of a car affects how well the car protects its occupants. It also determines how much damage and injury the car can inflict on other vehicles and their occupants. Cars with more mass, for example, will hit something with more force than a similar, but lighter, car.

CHALLENGE **Are some types of cars more dangerous than other types?**

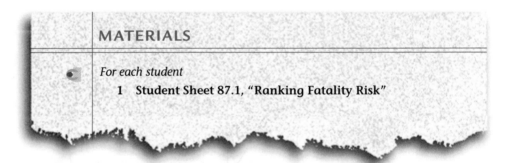

MATERIALS

For each student
1   **Student Sheet 87.1, "Ranking Fatality Risk"**

Accidents can be caused by driver error, distractions, weather, vehicle design, or a combination of factors.

PROCEDURE

1. Using the data tables below, discuss with your partner which vehicles have the highest and lowest risk for each kind of accident.

2. Use Student Sheet 87.1, "Ranking Fatality Risk," to help analyze the data. Record the type of vehicles that have the highest and lowest risk for each kind of accident.

3. With your group, discuss the limitations of the data in the tables. Make a list of information about traffic fatalities that the tables do not include.

Number of Fatalities per Billion Vehicle Miles*			
Vehicle Type	All accidents, any fatality in any vehicle	Rollover accidents occupant fatalities	Fixed object, occupant fatalities
Very small 4-door cars	20.6	1.1	4.0
Small 4-door cars	15.3	.8	2.9
Mid-sized 4-door cars	12.4	.8	2.6
Large 4-door cars	9.3	.5	2.1
Large pickup trucks	13.0	1.0	2.2
Mid-sized 4-door SUVs	16.7	4.4	2.6
Large 4-door SUVs	13.0	2.1	2.1
Minivans	10.6	1.1	1.4

Two-Vehicle Accidents: Number of Fatalities per Billion Vehicle Miles*		
Vehicle Type	Occupant, Fatalities	Fatalities in Other Vehicle
Very small 4-door cars	7.1	2.7
Small 4-door cars	4.9	2.2
Mid-sized 4-door cars	2.8	2.5
Large 4-door cars	1.7	2.2
Large pickup trucks	1.3	4.9
Mid-sized 4-door SUVs	2.2	4.5
Large 4-door SUVs	1.3	4.3
Minivans	1.8	3.0

U.S. Dept of Transportation: National Highway Traffic Safety Administration (NHTSA)

*Case vehicles are model year 1996–1999 with air bags, and the accidents occurred 1996–2000.

ANALYSIS

 1. How can the following aspects of a car's design help avoid accidents:

   a. mass and inertia?

   b. center of mass?

   c. braking distance?

2. Use the data from the tables to explain which vehicle type:

   a. is most likely to be in an accident that includes fatalities.

   b. is least likely to be in an accident that includes fatalities.

3. Use the data from the tables to explain which vehicle type in a two-car accident is most likely to cause a death:

   a. of people in the other vehicle.

   b. of its own occupants.

4. Use evidence from this and other activities in this unit to explain why mid-sized cars and SUVs have:

   a. different rollover fatality rates.

   b. the same fixed-object fatality rates.

5. Noah's family of four wants to buy a safe car. Which type of car would you recommend? Use evidence from the data tables in this activity and ideas from this unit to explain your decision.

6. **Reflection:** Americans 15–24 years old have almost twice the risk of dying in a motor vehicle accident as Americans aged 25–34. Why do you think the risks are so different for these two age groups?

ROLE PLAY

The severity of a car accident depends on many factors. These factors tend to fall into two categories: driving habits and vehicle characteristics. Because people's driving habits are harder to control than vehicle characteristics, some people think the best way to reduce the number of injuries and deaths caused by car accidents is to pass laws that standardize the features of noncommercial cars, such as their mass, bumper height, and front-end and roof stiffness.

CHALLENGE ▷ **Should noncommercial vehicles be more alike?**

MATERIALS

For each student
1   Student Sheet 88.1, "Discussion Web: Safety For All"

PROCEDURE

1. Decide which group member will play each of the roles shown on this and the next page.

2. Each person should read his or her role aloud while the rest of the group listens.

3. After each role is read, identify the evidence each character has presented.

4. Discuss whether each character's piece of evidence supports or does not support making cars more alike. Use Student Sheet 88.1, "Discussion Web: Safety For All," to sort the evidence.

   • Under the "Yes" column, explain how a particular piece of evidence *supports* making cars more alike.

   • Under the "No" column, explain how a particular piece of evidence *does not support* making cars more alike.

Hope Ezersky, founder of Families For Larger Cars

Both my legs were broken when a large SUV slid into my very small four-door sedan on a wet road. Now I drive a large family sedan so that I will have less chance of getting hurt if a car hits me again. I think all cars should be about the same mass so that the risk is even for everyone in an accident. Right now, larger passenger vehicles can weigh 1,000–2,000 pounds more than small ones. That means all vehicles do not hit with the same force. Since the average American family is three or four people, cars should be large enough to easily hold that many. So help make accidents fair by banning all small cars.

Damion Reese, President of Equitable Vehicles Now

I think some features of larger vehicles make driving more dangerous. With their higher centers of mass, SUVs and pickup trucks roll over more easily than ordinary passenger cars. Of all accident types, rollovers are most likely to lead to fatalities. In addition to putting their own occupants at risk, large SUVs, pickups, and vans put the occupants of other passenger cars at high risk. Large vehicles cause more damage in accidents because of their high mass, higher frames, and stiff front ends. All vehicles should have similar features to help avoid fatalities. Increased costs from making vehicles similar will be worthwhile if it makes the roads safer for everyone.

Hugo LaPierre, Physics Student and Teacher

Don't ban certain types of cars, ban certain kinds of drivers. Most accidents happen because people are bad drivers. I don't think people understand how much the braking distance changes when the road conditions change. As a result, people often drive too fast and too closely to other cars in the rain and snow. I always make sure to leave extra braking room when I drive. People also drive when they're sleepy or distracted. The worst ones drive under the influence of drugs and alcohol. I think we need to educate drivers more and pass laws requiring tougher and more frequent driving tests. The cost for the extra education can be spread out among all drivers.

Wilma Chang, Owner of Haul It, Inc.

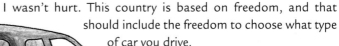

I think the current laws work for everyone. I haul lumber and other supplies in my free time, so I need a large pickup truck. Sometimes I use the truck to help a neighbor, pick something up, or move things for a local charity. If automakers redesign pickups to add more safety features, trucks will cost more for people like me who can't afford to pay more. I've never caused an accident, and the one time I was hit, I wasn't hurt. This country is based on freedom, and that should include the freedom to choose what type of car you drive.

ANALYSIS

1. Make a list of car features that contribute to the safety of the vehicle but are not the same in all vehicle classes. Explain how each feature contributes to the safety of the vehicle.

2. Write a letter to the head of the U.S. Senate Committee for Highway Safety, explaining your position on whether cars should be required by law to be alike. Use evidence to support your position and describe at least one trade-off of your decision.

Index

A **bold** page number identifies the page on which the term is defined.

A

ABS brakes, E51
acceleration
    graphing, **E15**
    Newton's Second Law,
      E21–24, E34
    units of measure, E21
accidents, cars. *See* automobiles,
  accidents.
air bags, E52–53
antilock brakes, E50–51
automobiles
    accidents
      crash testing, E55–57
      duration of collision,
        E16–18
      fatalities, E62–64
      speed, and collision force,
        E16–18
      speed, as a factor, E7–11
    braking distance, E41–44
    reaction time, effect on stop-
      ping distance, **E46**–48
    safety
      ABS brakes, E51
      air bags, E52–53
      antilock brakes, E50–51
      brakes, E50
      collapsible steering wheels,
       E54
      crash statistics, E63
      crumple zones, E53
      disc brakes, E50

      feature analysis, E4–6,
       E62–64
      features, E50–54
      safety cage, E53
      seat belts, E52
      standardized features,
       E65–68
      tires, E50
    speedometers, E7–8
    stopping distance, **E45**–48

B

balanced forces, **E33,** E37–40
brakes, E50
braking distance, **E41**
    effect of speed on, E42–44
    role in accidents, E41–44

C

cars. *See* automobiles.
collapsible steering wheels, E54
collisions. *See* automobiles,
  accidents.
crash statistics, E63
crash testing, E55–57
crashes. *See* automobiles,
  accidents.
crash-test dummies, E55–57
crumple zones, E53
curves, motion around, E25–28

D

deceleration, controlling, E49–54
disc brakes, E50

E

Endeavor, space shuttle, E41
equations
    net force, E34
    reaction distance, E46
    Newton's Second Law, E23–24
    speed, E7
    stopping distance, E46

F

fatalities in auto accidents, E62–64
First Law, E30–31
force, **E16**
    balanced forces, **E33,** E37–40
    and collisions, E16–18
    and mass, E19–20
    net force, **E33**
    Newton's Laws of Motion,
      E29–36
    unbalanced forces, **E34,**
      E37–40
    unit of measure, E21
formulas. *See* equations.
friction, **E31**
    and accident risk. *See* braking
      distance.
    and motion, E31–33

G

Galilei, Galileo, E30

I

inertia, **E25.**
    and mass, E25

    and motion, E25–28
    and Newton's First Law,
      E30–32
    passengers in an accident,
      E51–52

K

kilograms, E21
kilometers per hour, E7

L

Law of Action-Reaction, E35
Law of Inertia, E30–31

M

mass, **E19.**
    center of, **E58–61**
    and collisions, E19–20,
      E58–61
    and force, E19–20
    and inertia, E25
    unit of measure, E21
meters per second, E7
miles per hour, E7
motion
    around a curve, E25–28
    changes in, E16–18, E19–20,
      E21–24, E29–36
    laws governing. *See* Newton's
      Laws of Motion.
motion graphs, E12–15

N

net force, **E33**–34
Newton, Isaac, E29
newtons (N), E21
Newton's Laws of Motion
    First Law, E30–31

original text, E29
Second Law, E34
Third Law, E35

R

radar guns, E11
reaction distance, calculating, E46
reaction time, effect on stopping
    distance, **E46**–48

S

safety cage, E53
seat belts, E52
Second Law, E34
space shuttle Endeavor, E41
speed, **E7.** *See also* time and
    distance, measuring.
        as a cause of automobile
            accidents, E7–11
        and collision force, E16–18
        effect on braking distance,
            E42–44
        formula for calculating, E7
        graphing. See motion graphs.

measuring, E7–11
radar guns, E11
units of measure, E7
speedometers, E7–8
standardized safety features,
    E65–68
stopping distance, **E45–48**

T

Third Law, E35
time and distance, measuring. *See
    also* speed.
        model cart, E8–10
        motion graphs, E12–15
        radar gun, E11
tires, E50

U

unbalanced forces, **E34,** E37–40

V

vehicle types, E63

CREDITS

Abbreviations: t (top), m (middle), b (bottom), l (left), r (right), c (center)

All illustrations by Seventeenth Street Studios / Valerie Winemiller.

Cover (front): wind power generators: Digital Vision / Getty Images; cart: LabAids®, Inc.; (back): student hands: Lab-Aids®, Inc.

"Problem Solving" icon photo: ©Thom Lang / Corbis
"Talking It Over" icon photo: ©Michael Keller / Corbis

Unit title (E1) David Madison / Photodisc / Getty Images; Unit Opener (E2, E3): tl: Photodisc / Getty Images; tr: ©Jason Horowitz / zefa / Corbis; br: Jess Alford / Photodisc / Getty Images; bl: Steve Smith / Taxi / Getty Images; E7 Stockdisc Classic / Getty Images; E11 ©Joseph Sohm, ChromoSohm Inc. / Corbis; E16 TRL Ltd. / Photo Researchers, Inc.; E19 Photodisc / Getty Images; E21: l: ©Chris Trotman / Duomo / Corbis; r: ©Chris Trotman / NewSport / Corbis; E25 Lutz Bongarts / Getty Images News / Getty Images; E27: ©Jason Horowitz / zefa / Corbis; E29: l and r: Rare Book and Special Collections / Library of Congress; E31: l and r: Corbis; E32: l: David Madison / Photodisc / Getty Images; r: Steve Smith / Taxi / Getty Images; E33 Jess Alford / Photodisc / Getty Images; E34 Matt Campbell / AFP / Getty Images; E35 Indian Space Research Organisation / Photo Researchers, Inc.; E41 NASA / Photo Researchers, Inc.; E45 Patrick Molnar / Taxi / Getty Images; E47 Jim Reed / Photo Researchers, Inc.; E49 Corbis; E50: Courtesy of U.S. Representative, Frank R. Wolf (Va.); E51: tl: Martyn F. Chillmaid / Photo Researchers, Inc.; tr: David R. Frazier / Photo Researchers, Inc.; E53 Patti Conville / Getty Images; E54 Ryan McVay / Photodisc / Getty Images; E55 TRL Ltd. / Photo Researchers, Inc.; E56 Maximilian Stock Ltd. / Photo Researchers, Inc.; E62 Flying Colours Ltd / Digital Vision / Getty Images